GW00381630

A boy called Michael

A boy called Michael

A Popjustice Book
Illustrated by David Whittle

First published in Great Britain in 2006 by Friday Books
An imprint of The Friday Project Limited
83 Victoria Street, London SW1H 0HW

www.thefridayproject.co.uk
www.fridaybooks.co.uk

ISBN – 10 1 905548 07 9
ISBN – 13 978 1 905548 07 1

British Library Cataloguing in Publication Data

A catalogue record for this book is available
from the British Library

Designed and produced by Staziker Jones
www.stazikerjones.co.uk

The Publisher's policy is to use paper
manufactured from sustainable sources

This book belongs to

_____

I am ___ years old

My favourite Michael Jackson
song is ─────────

When I grow up, I want to be ─────

Here is my autograph!

_____

This is Michael.

Michael sings pop songs.

Michael sings songs so well that people call him the King of Pop.

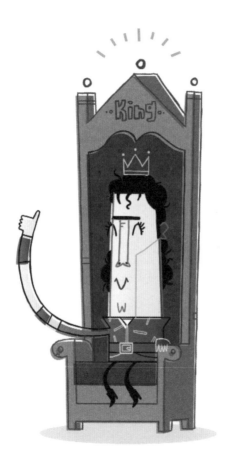

Michael likes to share his bed with boys.

You might think this is odd but that is because you are just ignorant.

In fact there are many things about Michael that seem strange, but are actually completely normal!

For example, sometimes Michael looks like he is walking forwards, but he is walking backwards.

Also, if you were to line up lots of pictures of Michael, you might think that he had changed himself lots, to look different.

You would be wrong to think that – most of this has happened by itself!

(Apart from one or two bits.)

Michael has been famous for a very long time.

It all started when he was five years old.

Michael came from a very big family, and he formed a band with some of his brothers.

Michael's dad was in charge of the band.

Sometimes Michael's dad was mean
to Michael.

"You are not good enough!" boomed
Michael's dad.

To cheer himself up, Michael made friends with a rat.

Rats are disgusting beasts which bite off people's faces and carry killer diseases but Michael did not mind this.

When he was a bit older, Michael made a record by himself.

It sold millions of copies and made Michael very famous.

In fact, every time Michael released an album, it was bought by millions of people.

Michael was still popular even when he dressed up to make himself look scary.

One of Michael's albums was called 'Bad'.

It was not bad – it was very good.

Another example of how things about Michael are not always how they seem!

Because Michael did not have very much fun when he was a young boy, he liked to make friends with young boys to make sure they had more fun than he did.

He invited them to his big house, where he had a theme park and a zoo.

Michael had a snake called Muscles. Sometimes guests to the house were allowed to play with Michael's snake.

Unfortunately – because they were just ignorant – some people thought that Michael might have been kissing his young boy friends.

This was not true!

But then the dad of one of Michael's little friends Jordan said that it WAS true!

So people got very confused!

Michael didn't like people being confused.

So, to stop any more confusion, Michael paid Jordan's dad lots of money.

After he did that, Jordan's dad stopped saying mean things, and everyone stopped being confused.

Thank goodness Michael was able to stop the confusion!

One day on stage Michael was performing a song and pretended to be Jesus.

This annoyed a boy called Jarvis.

Jarvis climbed on stage and waved his bottom around, but he was arrested for being ignorant.

Silly Jarvis!

Michael decided to get married to a girl called Lisa Marie.

Lisa Marie's father had been a very famous singer called Elvis Presley.

People were very interested in Michael's new wife.

Unfortunately the marriage did not last. Somehow Michael managed to carry on even though he must have been very upset.

After that, Michael released a new album of songs.

It did not sell as many copies as Michael's earlier albums.

This was because people were ignorant and did not understand that it was brilliant.

Because Michael loved children so much, he decided it was about time he had his own baby.

He called the baby Prince.

Michael liked to show off his son.

One day a boy called Martin made friends with Michael. Martin was a TV presenter.

"Can I interview you please?" said Martin.

"Yes as long as you are not mean and ignorant!" said Michael.

Martin made a very interesting TV programme. Unfortunately Michael did not like it.

These days Michael is just as famous as he ever was, but he does not sell as many albums as he did when he was younger.

Maybe if he sang a song as good as his old ones he would sell more records.

So that is the story of a boy called Michael.

And if you don't like him that is because you are just ignorant!

Michael Jackson and Jordy Chandler used to play together all the time but are not allowed to now.

Cut out Michael and his friend Jordy (be careful with the scissors!), stick them to your fingers and act out their special scenes.

Michael: Let's have a pyjama party.
Jordy: My Mum says I am not allowed.
Michael: Not even if I give you a billion dollars?

Have fun!

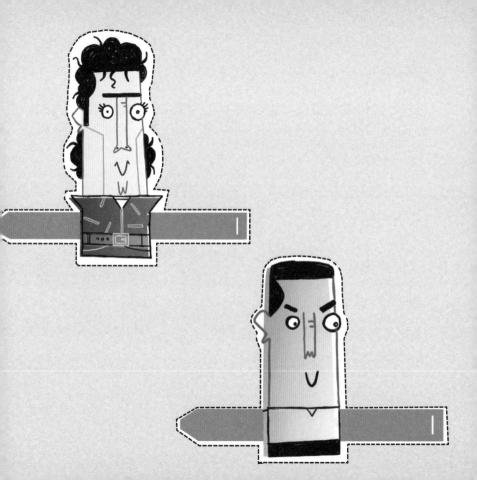

Loads more Popjustice Idols are waiting to say hello to you in your local bookshop - including Robbie Williams, Britney Spears, Eminem, Pete Doherty, Michael Jackson, Elton John, Take That and Madonna!
www.popjustice.com/idols

PLUS!

THE WEBSITE!
Daily updates, podcasts, videos, downloads, pop gossip, pop stuff, pop in general... Plus get Popjustice on your mobile phone!
www.popjustice.com

THE ALBUM!
The greatest pop album of all time, featuring AMAZING songs by AMAZING popstars, all mixed nicely together!
www.popjustice.com/album

THE CLUB NIGHT!
Two floors of unbelievable pop music, every week, in the centre of London town. We do not play stuff by Shayne Ward!
www.popjustice.com/club